Nature Did It First

Description

In this lesson, students discover that burrs stick to animal fur using tiny hooks, and they learn that Velcro was designed to mimic the way a burr works. Then students use the practice of biomimicry to design a solution to a problem: nature-inspired clothing that can help meet the needs of humans.

Alignment With the *Next Generation Science Standards*

Performance Expectations

1-LS1-1: Use materials to design a solution to a human problem by mimicking how plants and/or animals use their external parts to help them survive, grow, and meet their needs.

K-2-ETS1-2: Develop a simple sketch, drawing, or physical model to illustrate how the shape of an object helps it function as needed to solve a given problem.

Science and Engineering Practices	Disciplinary Core Ideas	Crosscutting Concept
Constructing Explanations and Designing Solutions Use tools and/or materials to design and/or build a device that solves a specific problem or a solution to a specific problem. Obtaining, Evaluating, and Communicating Information Read grade-appropriate texts and/or use media to obtain scientific and/or technical information to determine patterns in and/or evidence about the natural and designed world(s).	LS1.A: Structure and Function All organisms have external parts. Different animals use their body parts in different ways to see, hear, grasp objects, protect themselves, move from place to place, and seek, find, and take in food, water, and air. Plants also have different parts (roots, stems, leaves, flowers, fruits) that help them survive and grow. ETS1.B: Developing Possible Solutions Designs can be conveyed through sketches, drawings, or physical models. These representations are useful in communicating ideas for a problem's solutions to other people.	Structure and Function The shape and stability of structures of natural and designed objects are related to their function(s).

Note: The activities in this lesson will help students move toward the performance expectations listed, which is the goal after multiple activities. However, the activities will not by themselves be sufficient to reach the performance expectations.

Featured Picture Books

TITLE: ***Nature Did It First: Engineering Through Biomimicry***
AUTHOR: **Karen Ansberry**
ILLUSTRATOR: **Jennifer DiRubbio**
PUBLISHER: **Dawn Publications**
YEAR: **2020**
GENRE: **Dual Purpose**
SUMMARY: *This book explores the ways humans have looked to nature to solve problems. Each example in nature is paired with a playful poem, an example of how it has inspired innovation, and a question to the reader: "What other problems can be solved?"*

TITLE: ***Clothing Inspired by Nature***
AUTHOR: **Margeaux Weston**
PUBLISHER: **Pebble**
YEAR: **2020**
GENRE: **Non-Narrative Nonfiction**
SUMMARY: *Simple text and full-color photographs describe a variety of clothing, fabric, and technologies inspired by nature.*

Time Needed

This lesson will take several class periods. Suggested scheduling is as follows:

Session 1: Engage with Nature Did It First Read-Aloud, Part 1 and Explore with Burrs and Velcro

Session 2: Explain with Nature Did It First Read-Aloud, Part 2

Session 3: Elaborate with Clothing Inspired by Nature Read-Aloud and Card Sort

Session 4: Evaluate with Biomimicry Fashions

Materials

Per student:

- 1 Bunchem (Bunchems can be ordered on-line or purchased at stores such as Target or Walmart.)
- Small square of faux fur
- Hand lens
- Approx. 1-inch Velcro two-piece strip, non-adhesive
- Optional: 2 small googly eyes or a wallet-sized photo of each individual student in the class

SAFETY

- Caution students against putting Bunchems in their hair.
- Check with school nurse to make sure no students are allergic to feathers, wool, or other fabrics.
- Use caution when working with scissors (a potential sharp hazard) to avoid cutting or puncturing skin.
- Have students wash hands with soap and water after completing activities.

- Scissors
- Glue

Per class:

- 1 long-haired stuffed dog or other long-haired stuffed animal (in advance, cover it with enough Bunchems that each student can pull one off)
- Large variety of felt squares and other fabric samples
- Large variety of faux fur and leather squares and other natural-looking fabric materials
- Yarn, rickrack, small buttons, and a variety of other fabric notions
- Feathers (optional)

Student Pages

- Clothing Inspired by Nature Card Sort
- Paper Person Template
- Biomimicry Fashions (half sheet)
- STEM Everywhere

Background for Teachers

Biomimicry is the practice of designing materials, structures, and systems modeled on living things. This field of science is known as biomimetics. Scientists and engineers study nature and use its solutions to solve human problems. In this lesson, students observe burr models ("Bunchems" craft balls) and discover that the structure of a burr is directly related to its function—to attach to animal fur in order to aid seed dispersal. Then they observe Velcro strips using hand lenses and note the similarities to burrs. They learn how the structure and function of burrs inspired a Swiss inventor named George de Mestral to invent Velcro. He noticed how strongly cockleburs stuck to his pants after a walk through the woods, so he decided to look closely at them under a microscope. He observed that the burrs were covered in small hooks and that the hooks caught the loops in the fabric of his pants. This observation inspired him to design a loop-and-hook fastening system, patented in 1955 under the name Velcro.

Students learn how nature-inspired clothing has solved many human problems—from Olympians wearing swimsuits that mimic sharkskin, to waterproof fabric modeled after the leaves of a lotus plant, to strong and lightweight material inspired by spider silk. The science and engineering practice (SEP) of obtaining, evaluating, and communicating information is used as students listen to read-alouds about how humans use the practice of biomimicry to design solutions. Then they are challenged to design an article of clothing to solve a problem. Students share their designs using a paper doll model. These activities allow students to experience the SEP of constructing explanations and designing solutions, while addressing the crosscutting concept (CCC) of structure and function.

Learning Progressions

Following are the disciplinary core idea (DCI) grade band endpoints for grades K–2 and 3–5. These are provided to show how student understanding of the DCIs in this lesson will progress in future grade levels.

DCIs	Grades K–2	Grades 3–5
LS1.A: Structure and Function	• All organisms have external parts. Different animals use their body parts in different ways to see, hear, grasp objects, protect themselves, move from place to place, and seek, find, and take in food, water, and air. Plants also have different parts (roots, stems, leaves, flowers, fruits) that help them survive and grow.	• Plants and animals have both internal and external structures that serve various functions in growth, survival, behavior, and reproduction.
ETS1.B: Developing Possible Solutions	• Designs can be conveyed through sketches, drawings, or physical models. These representations are useful for communicating ideas for a problem's solutions to other people.	• At whatever stage, communicating with peers about proposed solutions is an important part of the design process, and shared ideas can lead to improved designs.

Source: Willard, T., ed. 2015. The NSTA quick-reference guide to the NGSS: Elementary school. Arlington, VA: NSTA Press.

engage

Nature Did It First Read-Aloud, Part 1

> Connecting to the Common Core
> **Reading: Informational Text**
> KEY IDEAS AND DETAILS: 1.1

Inferring

Introduce the author and illustrator of Nature Did It First: Engineering Through Biomimicry. Show students the cover and ask

? What do you think the word biomimicry means? (Answers will vary.)

? What does it mean to mimic something? (to copy it)

? What is the animal on the cover? (Answers will vary, but some students may recognize the lizard, a gecko, in the picture.)

? What do you think this book might be about? (Answers will vary.)

Then read the first poem, "Burr," on page 2.

Making Connections: Text to Self

After reading page 2, ask

? Have you ever had a burr stuck to your hair or clothing, or to a pet's hair? (Answers will vary.)

? What did it feel like? (Answers will vary.)

? Why do you think the burr stuck so well? (Answers will vary.)

AUTHOR KAREN ANSBERRY READING ALOUD

explore

Burrs

Tell students that you would like them to observe a burr very carefully in order to figure out how it sticks. Explain that real burrs can be painful to handle, but they can observe something that is a good model of a burr—a Bunchems craft ball. Show them a stuffed dog covered in Bunchems. Explain that the Bunchems stick to the toy in the same way that real burrs stick to a real dog, so they will be using the Bunchems as a model of a burr. Have students each pull a "burr" off the dog as you pass it around and give them each a

MODELING BURRS ON DOG FUR

piece of faux fur. Explain that the faux fur will serve as a model of an animal's fur. After they pull off the burr, they can experiment with getting it to stick to the faux fur. Caution them that the Bunchems can get tangled easily in hair, so they need to keep them away from everyone's hair.

Then explain that a scientific tool called a hand lens can help them get an even closer look at their burrs. Demonstrate the proper way to use a hand lens (holding the lens close to one eye while bringing the burr toward the hand lens until it comes into focus), and caution students that touching anything to the surface of the hand lens can scratch the lens. Pass out hand lenses to all students, and have them use the lenses to observe their burr more closely. Caution them again to not put the burr into anyone's hair!

After students have had time to observe the burrs, ask

? What did you notice? (Answers will vary.)

? What did the burr look like under the hand lens? (It had spikes or spines with tiny hooks on the ends.)

? Why do you think burrs in nature have parts that help them stick to things? (Answers will vary.)

? What problems might humans solve using their knowledge of the structures (parts) of burrs? (Answers will vary.)

? What are you wondering about burrs? (Answers will vary.)

Velcro

Next, give each student a small piece of the "hook" part of Velcro. Ask

? Does anyone know what this is? (a piece of Velcro)

Have them use a hand lens to observe it and compare it to the burr they observed. After students have had time to observe and explore with the Velcro, ask

? What did you notice? (Answers will vary.)

? What does the Velcro look like under the hand lens? (It had spikes or spines with tiny hooks on the ends.)

? How is the Velcro like the burr? (Answers will vary.)

? How is the Velcro different from the burr? (Answers will vary.)

? Think about the ways that you have used Velcro? What is "missing" from the Velcro? (the other piece)

? What are you wondering? (Answers will vary.)

VELCRO UP CLOSE

Next, give each student a small piece of the "loop" part of Velcro. Have them use a hand lens to observe it. Then have them put the two pieces of Velcro together and pull them apart. Ask

? What do you notice? (Answers will vary.)

? What does this part of Velcro look like? (It is covered with small loops.)

? How does the Velcro work with both parts? (The hooks attach to the loops.)

? What are you wondering? (Answers will vary.)

explain

Nature Did It First Read-Aloud, Part 2

Connecting to the Common Core
Reading: Informational Text
KEY IDEAS AND DETAILS: 1.1

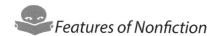 Features of Nonfiction

> **SEP: Obtaining, Evaluating, and Communicating Information**
> Read grade-appropriate texts to obtain scientific and/or technical information to determine patterns in and/or evidence about the natural and designed world(s).

Read the two-page spread "Hooks That Cling" on pages 4–5. Model using the glossary by asking students what they think the bold print words (engineer, technology, biomimicry) mean, and then look them up in the glossary. Then ask

? Why do some plants have burrs? (Burrs contain the plant's seeds.)

? What function (purpose) do the hooks on a burr serve? (They help them stick to fur or clothing.)

? How does this help this kind of plant survive and grow? (The burr is carried around until it falls off. The seeds inside fall out and grow new plants.)

? What structure (part) of a burr did George de Mestral mimic, or copy, to invent Velcro? (the hooks)

? What function (purpose) do the hooks on Velcro serve? (They stick to the loop side of the Velcro to hold things together.)

Point out the picture of the child's shoe at the top of page 5. Ask

? How is Velcro being used here? (to attach the strap to the shoe)

? What human problem does this solve? (It helps hold shoes onto your feet. It makes it easier and faster to fasten the shoe. It helps people who have difficulty tying their shoes.)

? What other ways does Velcro help humans meet their needs? (It gives humans an easy way to fasten things, like fastening a jacket, securing a watch to your wrist, closing pockets on backpacks, and hanging pictures.)

? Have you ever heard the expression, "Nature knows best"? (Answers will vary.)

> **CCC: Structure and Function**
> The shape and stability of structures of natural and designed objects are related to their function(s).

Explain that "nature knows best" is the idea behind the practice of biomimicry: mimicking, or copying, nature to solve problems. Life on Earth has existed for billions of years, and that is a long time for nature to figure out what works and what doesn't! So why not look to nature for answers to life's problems?

Engineers often look to nature to develop new technologies: tools or machines designed to help solve a problem. Engineers, and scientists, mimic the structures and functions of plants and animals when they are using nature to help them design new technologies.

Next, read a few of the other poems and the informational text that follows each one. Have students identify the structure of the plant or animal that was mimicked, or copied, for each technology. Discuss how that structure helps the animal or plant survive and grow. For example, read about how the gecko gave engineers the idea to design a super-sticky adhesive that sticks firmly and peels off easily. Then ask

? What structure (part) of a gecko did scientists and engineers mimic to design the adhesive? (the gecko's hairy toes)

? How do the gecko's hairy toes help it survive and grow? (The hairy toes allow them to stick to surfaces. When geckos want to move, they un-peel their toes. This gives them good climbing ability to find food or escape from predators.)

? What human problem does gecko-inspired adhesive solve? (It allows humans to stick objects or materials together without damage.)

 Turn and Talk

Ask the following question and allow students to talk with a partner or small group to share their ideas. Then have one person from each group share an idea with the class. Ask

? What other problems could be solved by mimicking geckos? (Answers will vary.)

Alternatively, read about how the pitcher plant gave engineers the idea for a slippery material that can be used to line ketchup bottles or coat airplane wings. Then ask

? What structure (part) of a pitcher plant did engineers mimic to design the slippery material? (the inner surface of the hanging pitcher or leaf)

? How does the inner surface of the pitcher plant's leaf help it survive and grow? (It is slippery, which keeps insects from climbing out. The pitcher plant needs the minerals it gets from the bodies of insects in order to survive and grow.)

? What human problem do pitcher plant–inspired materials solve? (Lining a bottle with it helps ketchup slide out. Coating airplane wings makes ice slide off.)

Ask the following question and allow students to talk with a partner or small group to share their ideas. Then have one person from each group share an idea with the class. Ask

? What other problems could be solved by mimicking pitcher plants? (Answers will vary.)

More examples are in the chart below.

Then explain that every structure of a plant or animal has a function. The shape of each structure is related to its function. Ask

? Why do burrs have the structure of curved hooks? (to stick to things)

? Why do burrs need to stick to things? In other words, how do they function to help the plant? (The burrs stick to things so they can be caried away and their seeds can be spread in other places.)

The structure (curved hook) is related to its function (sticking). Every structure in nature is shaped the best way for it to function properly. Nature knows best! Biomimicry is about mimicking what nature has already "figured out."

elaborate

Clothing Inspired by Nature Read-Aloud

Connecting to the Common Core
Reading: Informational Text
KEY IDEAS AND DETAILS: 1.1

Plant or Animal	Structures (Parts)	Functions (Purposes)	Technology
Little brown bat	Parts that help it use echolocation	Find food and fly in the dark	Cane that vibrates to help people who are blind find their way
Humpback whale	Bumpy flippers	Make tight turns in the water so they can catch food	Windmill blades and surfboard fins that turn more smoothly
Pill bug	Parts that help it roll up into a ball	Protect the soft inner part of its body	Pillbot (firefighting robot that rolls up to protect the equipment inside)
Kingfisher	Streamlined beak	Dive quickly to catch food	Nose for bullet train that could go through a tunnel without making a loud noise

Inferring

Introduce the title and author of Clothing Inspired by Nature. Ask

? What does the word inspire mean? (Answers will vary.)

Have students listen as you read aloud pages 4–7 about the invention of Velcro. Then ask

? The book says that nature inspires many things, like Velcro, that improve our lives. Now what are you thinking the word inspire means? (Answers will vary, but the glossary says that the word inspire means to influence or encourage someone to do something.)

? What inspired the invention of Velcro? (a burr or a cocklebur)

? Have you ever been inspired by nature? (Answers will vary.)

? Look around at what everyone is wearing—do you see any clothing that might have been inspired by nature? (Examples might include camouflage fabric inspired by plants, animal print fabric inspired by cheetahs or zebras, puffy coats inspired by birds or mammals, faux fur inspired by mammals, and Velcro shoe fasteners inspired by burrs.)

? Can you think of other examples of clothing inspired by nature? (Answers will vary.)

Clothing Inspired by Nature Card Sort

Before reading the rest of Clothing Inspired by Nature, pass out the Clothing Inspired by Nature Card Sort student pages, and have the students cut out the pictures of the plants and animals. Then have them match each picture to the clothing invention it inspired. They will have the opportunity to move their cards as you read the rest of the book.

Next, read pages 8–19 aloud. After reading each two-page spread, discuss each invention and its inspiration and have students move their cards if necessary. When finished, students can

Invention	Inspiration
1. Warm coat	Polar bear fur
2. Fabric that blends in with the surroundings	A squid's color-changing skin
3. Swimsuit that helps people swim super-fast	Shark skin
4. Patches for hands and feet that help people climb walls	Gecko feet
5. Shoes that are strong but lightweight	Spider silk
6. Waterproof coating for fabric	Leaves of the lotus plant

SORTING THE CARDS

glue the pictures to the correct place on the student pages. Answers are in the chart below.

After students have glued the pictures onto the student pages, invite them to think about how the plants and animals on the cards use their parts to help them survive and grow. Have them share their thinking. Examples could include the following:

- A polar bear's fur allows it to survive in extreme cold.
- A squid's skin changes color to help it hide and stay safe.
- A shark's skin helps it swim fast to catch food and stay safe.
- A gecko's feet help it climb to catch food and stay safe.
- A spider's silk helps it catch food.
- A lotus plant's waterproof leaves allow it to survive and grow in water.

Then invite students to think about how the nature-inspired clothing inventions help meet human needs. Have them share their thinking. Examples could include the following:

- A polar-bear inspired coat keeps a person warm in cold weather.
- A squid-inspired fabric helps people hide from danger.

- A shark-inspired swimsuit helps people swim faster.
- Gecko-inspired patches can help people climb.
- Spider silk–inspired shoes protect people's feet and help them get around faster.
- Lotus-inspired fabric coating helps people keep dry.

Making Connections: Text to Self

Then ask

? What was your favorite clothing invention in the book? Why? (Answers will vary.)

? What is a useful article of clothing that you have worn? What made it useful? What problem did it solve? (Answers will vary.)

evaluate

Biomimicry Fashions

Then tell students that they are going to have an opportunity to practice biomimicry by designing something everyone uses every day ... clothing! In the United States, people spend billions of dollars on clothing and footwear every year. The fashion industry relies on the invention of new technologies such as the sewing machine, the zipper, Velcro, and new kinds of fabric. More and more, fashion designers and engineers who design new technologies for the fashion industry look to nature for inspiration.

> **SEP: Constructing Explanations and Designing Solutions**
> Use tools and/or materials to design and/or build a device that solves a specific problem or solution to a specific problem.

Students will be working as fashion designers who look to nature for inspiration. They will be

designing an article of clothing based on the structure of a plant or animal. The clothing could be a shirt, pants, dress, coat, headwear, footwear, safety gear, or even an entire outfit.

 *Word Web*

Show students the Paper Person Template student page. The paper person will be their "model" for the article of clothing. They will be able to choose from a variety of materials to design and make the clothing to fit their paper person. Explain that when designing something, it is a good idea to brainstorm ideas first. On the board, start a word web by writing "What problems can clothing solve?" inside a circle. Have students brainstorm problems that clothing, headwear, footwear, and so on can solve, and then write their ideas around the circle.

Some problems that clothing might solve include the following:

- Keeping you warm
- Keeping you cool
- Keeping you dry
- Helping you swim faster
- Helping you run faster
- Helping you hide or camouflage
- Helping you stand out or look fashionable
- Protecting you from the Sun
- Protecting you from wind
- Protecting you from harm or danger

Then give each student a paper person and invite them to think about a problem that clothing could solve for their imaginary person. Ask

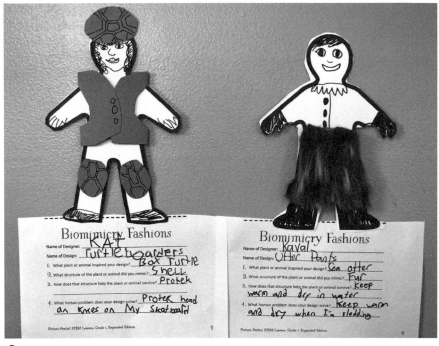

BIOMIMICRY FASHIONS

? What structure of a plant or animal could you look to for inspiration to solve the problem? (Answers will vary.)

Allow students to look at the choices of fabrics and natural materials they can choose from, then have them start designing an article of clothing (or a complete outfit if they wish). Have them use care with scissors when cutting fabric. They can color in hair, draw a face, glue on googly eyes, or cut out pictures of their own faces from school photos and glue them to the heads of the paper people.

Connecting to the Common Core
Writing
RESEARCH TO BUILD AND PRESENT KNOWLEDGE: 1.8

 Writing

When students have finished designing their clothing for the paper people, pass out the

Biomimicry Fashions student page where students will provide the following information about their design:

Name of Designer

Name of Design

1. What plant or animal inspired your design?
2. What structure of the plant or animal did you mimic?
3. How does that structure help the plant or animal survive?
4. What human problem does your design solve?

Finally, you can have a "Biomimicry Fashion Show" and have each student present their paper person to the class (a "runway" down the center of the room is fun!). You may want to emcee the fashion show by announcing each designer and their design as they walk their paper person down the runway. You could use the information from the students' Biomimicry Fashions sheets to do this in a fun way.

For example,

"And now we have Jax showing off his latest designer look: The Polar Coat. This full-length faux fur coat was inspired by the polar bear. A polar bear's fur helps it survive by protecting it from extreme cold. This extremely fashionable coat will help keep you "bear-y" warm!"

After the show, have students attach the Biomimicry Fashions half sheet to their paper person and display them on a bulletin board or in the hallway.

STEM Everywhere

Give students the STEM Everywhere student page as a way to involve their families and extend their learning. They can do the activity with an adult helper and share their results with the class. If students do not have access to the internet at home, you may choose to have them complete this activity at school.

Continued

Opportunities for Differentiated Instruction

This box lists questions and challenges related to the lesson that students may select to research, investigate, or innovate. Students may also use the questions as examples to help them generate their own questions. These questions can help you move your students from the teacher-directed investigation to engaging in the science and engineering practices in a more student-directed format.

Extra Support

For students who are struggling to meet the lesson objectives, provide a question and guide them in the process of collecting research or helping them design procedures or solutions.

Extensions

For students with high interest or who have already met the lesson objectives, have them choose a question (or pose their own question), conduct their own research, and design their own procedures or solutions.

After selecting one of the questions in this box or formulating their own questions, students can individually or collaboratively make predictions, design investigations or surveys to test their predictions, collect evidence, devise explanations, design solutions, or examine related resources. They can communicate their findings through a science notebook, at a poster session or gallery walk, or by producing a media project.

Research

Have students brainstorm researchable questions:

? What are some uses for Velcro?

? What are some other examples of biomimicry?

? What are some other examples of nature-inspired fashions?

Investigate

Have students brainstorm testable questions to be solved through science or math:

? How much weight can Velcro hold?

? How could you test some natural materials to see if they are waterproof?

? Compare and contrast the structures of birds to the structures of airplanes. What is the same? What is different?

Innovate

Have students brainstorm problems to be solved through engineering:

? Can you think of a new use for Velcro?

? Can you design a robot based on the structures of a plant?

? Can you design a robot based on the structures of an animal?

Clothing Inspired by Nature Card Sort

Biomimicry is a way of mimicking, or copying, nature to solve problems. Designers often look to nature for inspiration when inventing solutions.

Directions: Cut out the nature pictures from the third page and match each one to the clothing invention it inspired.

Clothing Invention	Inspiration From Nature
1. Warm coat	
2. Fabric that blends in with the surroundings	
3. Swimsuit that helps people swim super-fast	

National Science Teaching Association

Clothing Inspired by Nature
Card Sort (page 2)

4. Patches for hands and feet that help people climb walls	
5. Shoes that are strong but lightweight	
6. Waterproof coating for fabric	

Clothing Inspired by Nature
Card Sort (page 3)

National Science Teaching Association

Paper Person Template

Biomimicry Fashions

Name of Designer: _____

Name of Design: _____

1. What plant or animal inspired your design? _____

2. What structure of the plant or animal did you mimic? _____

3. How does that structure help the plant or animal survive? _____

   _____

4. What human problem does your design solve? _____

   _____

- -

Biomimicry Fashions

Name of Designer: _____

Name of Design: _____

1. What plant or animal inspired your design? _____

2. What structure of the plant or animal did you mimic? _____

3. How does that structure help the plant or animal survive? _____

   _____

4. What human problem does your design solve? _____

   _____

National Science Teaching Association

Name: _____

STEM Everywhere

Dear Families,

At school, we have been learning about **biomimicry**—the practice of looking to nature for inspiration to solve human problems. We explored how burrs stick to fabric or fur, and we learned how they inspired the invention of Velcro. To find out more, ask your learner the following questions and discuss their answers:

- What did you learn?

- What was your favorite part of the lesson?

- What are you still wondering?

 At home, you can talk about how superhero costumes are often inspired by nature. Then watch some National Geographic Kids "Amazing Animals" videos together. Scan the QR code or go to *https:// kids.nationalgeographic.com/videos/amazing-animals* to access the videos. These short videos can give you inspiration for designing your own superhero costume!

After watching some of the videos, think about the animal structures, or parts, you observed and how they might inspire a superhero costume. Brainstorm ideas, then draw and label your superhero costume in the box below.